This
Gruffalo and Friends
Annual belongs to

Sweet heart

First published 2016 by Macmillan Children's Books
an imprint of Pan Macmillan
20 New Wharf Road, London N1 9RR
Associated companies throughout the world
www.panmacmillan.com

ISBN 978-1-5098-1509-8

Based on the bestselling picture books *The Gruffalo, The Gruffalo's Child, Room on the Broom, The Snail and the Whale,
Monkey Puzzle, Charlie Cook's Favourite Book, A Squash and a Squeeze* and *The Smartest Giant in Town*
by Julia Donaldson and Axel Scheffler

Editorial: Amanda Li
Design: Dan Newman
Photography: Stuart Cox pages 14-17, 22-23, 46-47. Cast group photographs on pages 30-31 © Steve Ullathorne.
Portrait of Julia Donaldson on page 30 © Alex Rumford. Portrait of Axel Scheffler on page 44 © Liam Jackson

Shutterstock stock photography: Alexander Raths – 53tl, Alexius Sutandio – 28br, Anri Gor – 52mr,
ARENA Creative – 29mr, davemhuntphotography – 19br & 29tl, defpicture – 36br, kenkistler – 18br, nevenm – 37tr,
odd-add – 28tl, Ondrej Prosicky – 37ml, Panu Ruangjan – 36tl, Philip Ellard – 18tr, Rudmer Zwerver – 19ml,
seawhisper – 18ml, Seb c'est bien – 28mr, Sementer – 19tr, Subbotina Anna – 52tl, Suede Chen – 36ml,
VanderWolf Images – 53mr, Vladimir Wrangel – 29bl, worldswildlifewonders – 37br

1 3 5 7 9 8 6 4 2

A CIP catalogue record for this book is available from the British Library.

Printed in Italy

Contents

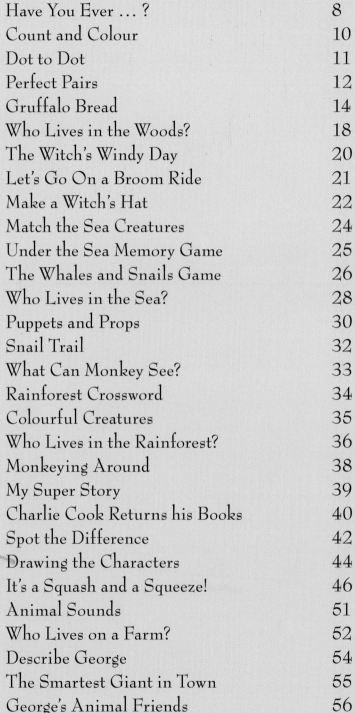

Story Match

Oh help! Oh no! It's a Gruffalo!

But which book does he come from?
Can you draw a line from each of the
other characters to their stories?

JULIA DONALDSON · AXEL SCHEFFLER
The Snail and the Whale

2

JULIA DONALDSON · AXEL SCHEFFLER
THE GRUFFALO

1

a

b

c

JULIA DONALDSON · AXEL SCHEFFLER
Charlie Cook's Favourite Book

3

d

JULIA DONALDSON · AXEL SCHEFFLER
Room on the Broom

4

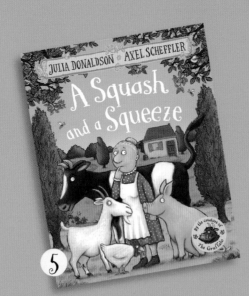

A Squash and a Squeeze
JULIA DONALDSON • AXEL SCHEFFLER

5

e

g

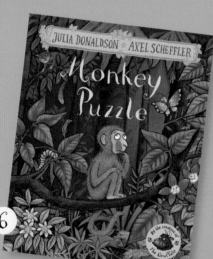

Monkey Puzzle
JULIA DONALDSON • AXEL SCHEFFLER

6

f

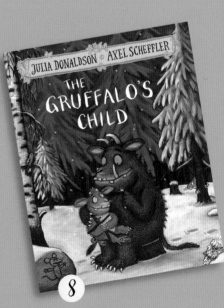

THE GRUFFALO'S CHILD
JULIA DONALDSON • AXEL SCHEFFLER

8

The Smartest GIANT in Town
JULIA DONALDSON • AXEL SCHEFFLER

7

h

Answers on page 61.

Have You Ever ...?

Colour in each leaf from the deep dark wood if you have ever ...

... climbed a tree.

... heard an owl hoot.

... walked across a log.

... spent the night in the woods.

... found a pine cone.

... played with a stick.

... made a snowman.

... looked up at the moon.

... seen a fox.

Have you really?

... scared a Gruffalo!

9

Count and Colour

Look at the pictures and colour in the correct number that answers each question.

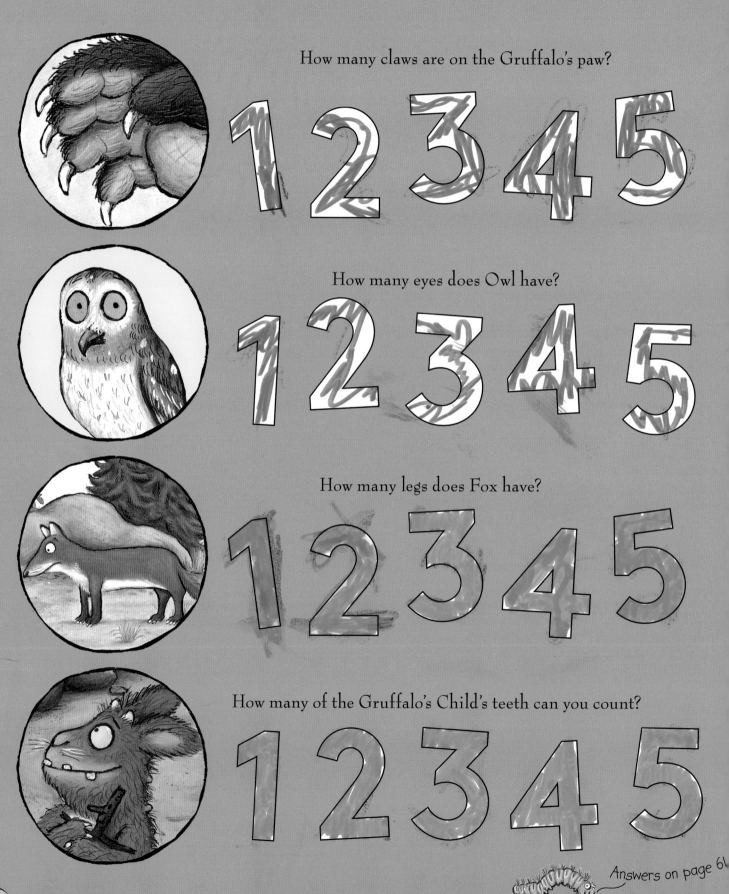

How many claws are on the Gruffalo's paw?

1 2 3 4 5

How many eyes does Owl have?

1 2 3 4 5

How many legs does Fox have?

1 2 3 4 5

How many of the Gruffalo's Child's teeth can you count?

1 2 3 4 5

Answers on page 61

Dot to Dot

Who is nibbling on a nut? Join the dots to find out.
Then add whiskers and a tail and colour in your picture.

That looks yummy!

Gruffalo

Perfect Pairs

Try this fun memory game for two players and see how many pairs you can find.

You will need:

- 16 playing cards (or cut up some paper into pieces that are just big enough to cover each picture)

Frog

Owl

Mouse

Gruffalo's Child

Fox

Snake

Snow Gruffalo

Snow Gruffalo

How to play:

1. Cover each picture with a playing card or piece of paper.
2. Player 1 picks up two cards, one from the left page and one from the right. If the two pictures underneath match, it's a perfect pair and the player keeps the cards. If not, put the cards back.
3. Now it's Player 2's turn to pick up two cards.
4. The winner is the person at the end who has found the most pairs.

Frog

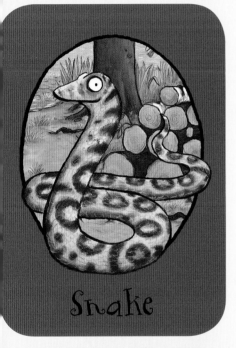

Snake

Fox

Mouse

Gruffalo's Child

Owl

Gruffalo

Gruffalo Bread

Would you like to make bread rolls which look like snakes, owls and the Gruffalo's feet? They not only look good – they taste good!

You will need:

- 500g strong white or wholemeal bread flour
- 1 sachet fast action dried yeast
- 1 ½ teaspoons of salt
- 320ml warm water
- 25g soft butter
- 2 teaspoons sugar
- decorations: black olives, sesame seeds, poppy seeds
- a beaten egg and pastry brush
- small pair of safety scissors
- 2 greased baking trays
- a grown-up helper

Make the dough:

1. Wash your hands. Put the flour into a mixing bowl with the salt, sugar and the yeast.

2. Rub the butter into the flour with your fingertips until all the lumps of butter have gone. Then gradually pour in the warm water, mixing it into a dough with a wooden spoon. Once all the water is mixed in, use your hands to form the dough into a ball.

3. Shake some flour onto a work surface. Place your ball of dough onto the flour and get ready for the fun part – kneading the dough!

4. First, press the dough with the bottom part of your hand, then fold it over towards you with your fingers. Keep pressing and folding the dough like this for at least ten minutes (you can stop for a break if you want). The kneading makes the dough nice and stretchy.

5. Place the dough into a bowl, cover with a tea towel and leave it in a warm place for one hour. It will rise and be bigger than before. Now it's time to make your rolls.

Find out how on the next page!

Make Owl

1. Take a handful of dough and roll into an oval for the owl's body. Make two smaller ovals and flatten them slightly for the owl's wings. Use a pastry brush dipped into the beaten egg to stick the wings to the sides of the body.

2. Take two tiny pieces of dough and roll into small balls. Flatten them and use beaten egg to stick them onto the top of the body for the eyes. Add two small pieces of chopped olive for the pupils and cut a triangular piece of olive for the beak. Push into the dough.

3. Take another two small pieces of dough, shape them into triangles and make two snips at the wide ends with your scissors. Shape into three claws and stick both feet to the bottom of the body with the beaten egg.

4. Finally, brush the owl all over with the beaten egg. Make tiny snips into the owl's body with the points of your scissors to look like fluffy feathers. Scatter some sesame seeds onto the wings or use your scissors to score lines on them.

Make a Gruffalo's Foot

1. Take a handful of dough and shape it into a Gruffalo's foot – a rectangle that is slightly wider at one end.

2. Make three 1cm snips at the widest end with your scissors. Form the dough into four claws with pointed ends.

3. Brush with beaten egg, then scatter with seeds or add a furry texture by snipping the top of the foot with scissors.

Make Snake

1. Roll a large handful of dough into a long, slim snake. Shape one end into a head and make two little holes at either side for the eyes. Place pieces of olive into the holes. Bend the snake into a shape – either a long, winding snake or a coiled-up snake.

2. Brush the snake with egg and sprinkle with seeds. You can also use your scissors to make patterns on the body of the snake.

Sssssssso tasty!

To Cook

Finally, place your rolls onto the greased baking trays. There should be a good space between each roll as they will get bigger as they bake. Bake for about 15 minutes in a hot oven at 200°C (190°C fan) or Gas Mark 6. When your rolls are golden brown on top, they should be ready. Eat warm, with butter. Yum!

17

Owls

Owls can fly very, very quietly. This helps them to catch mice and insects to eat when they are out hunting at night. All owls have large eyes and strong claws called talons, which help them to catch and hold their prey. Most owls make a low hooting noise, but they can also screech, whistle and hiss.

Squirrels

Have you ever seen a squirrel running up a tree? Squirrels can run fast and jump easily from branch to branch. They use their large bushy tails to help them balance. Tree squirrels build a nest called a drey high up in a tree. The nest is made of twigs and is about the size of a football.

Deer

Some woods have herds of deer living in them. Deer have long strong legs which help them run fast and jump high. They are also very good at swimming. A male deer is called a stag. Stags have hard antlers on their heads which they sometimes use for fighting with other stags. They grow new antlers every year.

the Woods?

Bats

Like owls, bats are also night-time creatures. When it is dark, bats come out to fly and catch insects to eat. They like to find a good spot in a tree or a cave to make their home in. This is called their roost. They hang upside down when they're resting – but they never fall down and they don't even get dizzy!

Mice

Look closely and you might see a little wood mouse running along the ground. Wood mice are brown with large ears, large feet and a long tail. They live in underground homes called burrows which they dig themselves. This is where they make their nests and store their food.

Foxes

Foxes come out at night to meet each other and to hunt for food. They can be really noisy. Sometimes foxes bark and growl, and at other times they make loud screeching noises. Foxes have pointed ears, a bushy tail and whiskers on their faces. They also have whiskers on their legs! These whiskers help them to find their way around easily in the dark.

Can you think of any other animals that live in the woods?

The Witch's Windy Day

It's very windy and some of the witch's things have blown away. Can you help her and her animal friends to get them back?

Draw:

- the witch's hat
- the spotty bow in her hair
- her wand
- the twigs on her broom
- the wart on her nose
- her missing shoe
- her cauldron

Now colour in the picture.

Let's Go On a Broom Ride

The witch is going for a broomstick ride. On the way she wants to pick up the bird – but she doesn't want to bump into the dragon! Can you find a safe route between the clouds?

START

FINISH

Answer on page 61.

Make a Witch's Hat

*The witch had a cat
and a very tall hat.*

You will need:

- 2 large sheets of stiff black paper or thin card: one size A2, and one A3. Or use white card and paint the hat black when finished.
- scissors
- sticky tape
- glue or double-sided tape
- a light-coloured pencil or crayon
- a large dinner plate
- decorations: ribbon, wool
- a grown-up helper

How to make:

1. Roll the A2 sheet of paper into a large pointed cone shape. Make sure the open end is big enough to fit easily onto the largest part of your head. Stick the cone together loosely with sticky tape.

2. Trim the bottom of the cone with scissors so that it is level and can stand up on a table. Now make sure your hat still fits onto your head. You can adjust the sticky tape to make it bigger if you need to. When you are happy with the fit, use glue or sticky tape to firmly stick down the long edge of the cone.

3. Now for the hat rim. First make sure your dinner plate is a few centimetres bigger than the base of your cone. Place the plate onto the A3 sheet of paper and draw around it. Cut out the large circle.

4. Place the cone onto the middle of the card circle and draw around it.

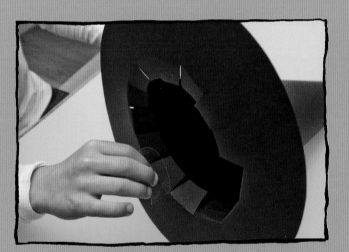

5. Draw another smaller circle about 2cm inside the cone outline you have just drawn. Then cut it out. This is quite tricky, so you might want to ask a grown-up to help you.

6. Make little flaps by cutting from the inside of your hat rim to the pencil line you drew around the base of your cone. Space the cuts about 2cm apart. Bend the flaps up and press them firmly one by one inside the large end of the cone. Use strips of tape to stick them down.

7. Your hat is ready to wear! If you like, you can decorate it with a colourful paper band or tie a ribbon bow around it. What about getting some wool and making the witch's plait to stick to the back of the hat? You'll be more than ready to go on a broom ride!

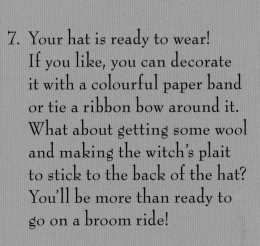

Wow! What a smart hat!

Match the Sea Creatures

A snail meets a whale and together they go on a wonderful journey.
They spot lots of different sea creatures along the way.
Can you draw lines to match the names to the pictures?

Starfish Lobster Crabs Octopus Dolphins

Fish Turtle Seals Seagull Penguins

Answers on page 61.

Under the Sea Memory Game

Look carefully at this picture of creatures that live in the sea.
Now cover the picture and see if you can answer the questions below.

Is there a whale in the picture?
What colour is the octopus?
How many sharks are in the picture?
Is there a starfish in the picture?
How many yellow stripy fish are there?

Now look at the picture again.
How many did you get right?

The Whales and Snails Game

The whales would like to take some snails on a lovely swim across the sea. Which whale will be the first to collect six snails and swim away?

You will need:

- Two players – whales A and B
- Two differently coloured counters
- A coin
- A pencil

START

1

2

3

1 2 3 4 5 6

A

How to play:

1. Decide who will be whale A and who will be whale B. Both whales put a counter onto the START rock.
2. The two whales take turns to flip the coin.
   - If your coin lands heads up, you can make two moves.
   - If your coin lands tails up, you can move only once.

   A move means that you can jump from one rock to a neighbouring rock. Every time you land on a numbered rock with snails on it, colour the small snail shape with the same number on your whale picture.
3. The aim is to land once on each of the rocks numbered 1-6. You can land on the rocks in any order you like.
4. The first whale to colour all six snails wins the game. If you want to play the game again, instead of colouring in the snails, just write down the rock number on a piece of paper each time you land on one.

27

Who Lives in the Sea?

Whales

Whales are the biggest animals in the world and the blue whale is the largest of them all.
Even though whales live in the sea they cannot breathe underwater. They come up to the surface of the water to breathe, first blowing the air out through blowholes in the top of their heads.
It makes a huge water spray!

Dolphins

Dolphins travel together in groups called pods. Like whales, they use blowholes on their heads to breathe air. Dolphins 'speak' to each other by making clicking and whistling sounds. They love to play and can sometimes be seen riding waves and jumping high out of the water.

Sharks

Sharks are large fish that can swim very fast. They have an incredible sense of smell which helps them to find food. Some sharks eat plants and have rounded teeth while other sharks eat sea creatures and have sharp, pointed teeth. Sharks have many rows of teeth. If they lose a tooth, another moves forward to replace it!

Crabs

All crabs have an outer shell, eight legs and a pair of front claws, which they use to catch and pick up food. If you've ever seen a shell that seems to be walking on legs, that is because a tiny crab called a hermit crab is living inside it. The shell makes a safe, cosy home for the little crab.

Octopuses

All octopuses have eight tentacles which they use to move themselves through the water. Most octopuses have clever ways to escape from attackers. They can squirt black ink at a creature to scare it. Octopuses can also change colour, which helps them to hide from danger.

Sea Snails

There are many different types of sea snail. Some are tiny, just the size of a pea, while others are even bigger than your hand. Unlike land snails, sea snails can breathe underwater. They have lots of tiny teeth which they use for grinding and eating sea plants. Some of the bigger sea snails can eat fish.

Can you think of any other creatures that live in the sea?

Puppets and Props
by Julia Donaldson

These days, when I am not writing, I am often out and about performing my stories at book festivals and in theatres. My husband Malcolm and my sister Mary act with me, as do two professional actors called Joanna and James. I like to invite children from the audience to join in, and sometimes even their teachers! Puppets, props and costumes play an important part, too.

When I first started reading my books to children in libraries and schools, I had a Gruffalo puppet that I used to help tell the story. But now when we perform our shows the real Gruffalo comes along instead!

We still use puppets to help act out other parts though. We have some lovely puppets for *A Squash and a Squeeze*, which were specially made. It was very important that they looked like Axel Scheffler's original illustrations. The goat, the pig and the cow have handles so they can be moved around the stage. The pig's mouth can open and close, and the hen has a hidden button which makes her wings flap.

Costumes can be a really good way to help you get into character. I enjoy playing the mouse in *The Gruffalo*, and wear mouse ears and a tail. Last year I added to my costume and wore a mouse-coloured coat too.

Malcolm acts the part of the fox and wears a smart bushy tail. Mary plays the owl. She has a feathered mask to give her big owl-like eyes and a beak. She also wears a brown cardigan with big sleeves that make good wings.

I have a special room in my house where I keep all my puppets, other props and costumes. An artist called Peter Monkman painted a picture of me sitting in it. You can see the painting in the National Portrait Gallery, in London. As well as all the props, I like the way the pencil and notebook in my hands give a clue to my story writing too.

Snail Trail

Choose a snail and follow its trail with
your finger to find out where it is going.

Which place would you like to visit?

What Can Monkey See?

What has Monkey spotted in the rainforest?
Draw what you think Monkey is looking at.

Rainforest Crossword

2 down

3 across

2 across

Which creatures live in the rainforest with Monkey?

Use the picture clues to complete the crossword. Some letters have been filled in to help you.

1 down

Answers on page 61.

4 across

6 across

5 down

7 across

34

Colourful Creatures

Look at all these colourful creatures! They are all a little bit different from one another, but can you spot the creature that looks exactly like …

… this butterfly?   1   2   3   4

… this bug?   1   2   3   4   5   6

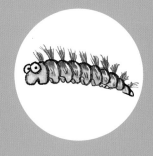 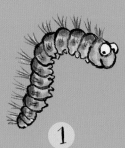 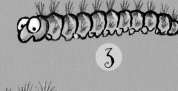 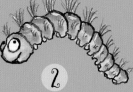 

… this caterpillar?   1   2   3   4   5

… this frog?   1   2   3   4

Answers on page 61.

Parrots

Bright, colourful parrots swoop through the trees, squawking loudly. Parrots eat seeds, nuts, fruit and insects and they use their strong curved beaks to crack shells and break up their food. They live in groups called flocks.

Frogs

In the rainforest you can always hear the sound of frogs croaking and chirping. Many frogs here are brightly coloured – yellow, blue, orange, green and red. Some rainforest frogs even have poison on their skin to protect themselves from animals that want to eat them.

Crocodiles

Look very carefully at the river and you might see two big eyes looking out above the water. It's a crocodile, watching and waiting for its next meal. It will snap up insects, fish, birds and small animals with its sharp teeth and strong jaws. It can also swim very fast using its long tail.

he Rainforest?

Chameleons

The chameleon sits very still on a branch – then *whoosh!* It shoots out its long tongue so fast that it can catch an insect before it flies away. Another amazing thing about chameleons is that they can change their skin colour. Many chameleons become more brightly coloured when they are frightened or excited.

Butterflies

Butterflies are probably the most beautiful insects in the rainforest. They have so many different colours and patterns on their incredible wings. Most butterflies feed from flowers. They have a long tongue that goes down into the flower and sucks up the sweet nectar from inside.

Monkeys

There are many different types of monkey in the rainforest. Spider monkeys use their long arms and tails to help them swing from branch to branch. Marmosets are so tiny that you could easily hold one in your hand. Howler monkeys have the loudest calls of any animal in the world!

Can you think of any other creatures that live in the rainforest?

Monkeying Around

Jokes for getting jolly in the jungle!

Where do frogs leave their coats?

In the croakroom.

What are monkeys' favourite biscuits?

Chocolate chimp cookies.

How do you catch a monkey?

Climb a tree and act like a banana.

What's grey, lives in the rainforest but never gets wet?

An elephant with an umbrella.

What are frogs' favourite sweets?

Lolli-hops.

What's the best thing to do if an elephant sneezes?

Get out of its way!

What is smaller than an ant's dinner?

An ant's mouth.

What do you call an elephant that never has a bath?

A smellyphant.

What's the biggest ant in the world?

An eleph-ant.

My Super Story

Charlie Cook has a favourite book,
which is all about other books.

What do *you* like reading about?
Design your own book cover
for a story you would like to read.

Charlie Cook Returns his Books

Charlie Cook is on his way to the library.
What will happen along the way?
Follow the path and complete the tasks.

1. Rowena Reddalot the frog likes books as much as Charlie. Can you make a sound like a frog?

1

2. Charlie meets a pirate with a parrot. "Hello," says Charlie. What do they reply? Fill in the bubbles.

2

3

3. Watch out, Charlie, there's a crocodile about! How many teeth has it got? Count them and write the number.

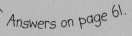
Answers on page 61.

40

5. Charlie looks up at the sky. He sees an alien spaceship whizzing by. Can you draw the aliens inside?

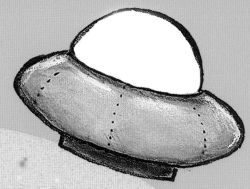

5

6. Three very cross bears are looking for someone. "Who's had our porridge?" they say to Charlie. Was it:

a. Cinderella? ☐

b. Snow White? ☐

c. Goldilocks? ☐

6

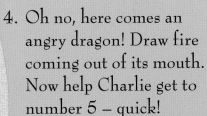

4. Oh no, here comes an angry dragon! Draw fire coming out of its mouth. Now help Charlie get to number 5 – quick!

4

7. At last! The library. How many books is Charlie returning? Write the number in the box.

7

Once upon a time there was a boy called Charlie Cook
Who curled up in a cosy chair and read his favourite book . . .

Difference

Look at the two pictures carefully.
Can you find six differences between them?

Answers on page 61.

Drawing the Characters
by Axel Scheffler

When I first get sent one of Julia's stories, I have a think about how each character might look and then start to draw. I begin with rough sketches. I draw the characters lots and lots of times, and by the time I do my final artwork for each book, you'd be surprised at how much some of them have changed …

The Gruffalo

I think Julia had originally imagined the Gruffalo to be more alien-like, but the word 'Gruffalo' reminded me of 'buffalo' so I drew him with horns and a tail. He started off on all fours too, but ended up walking upright.

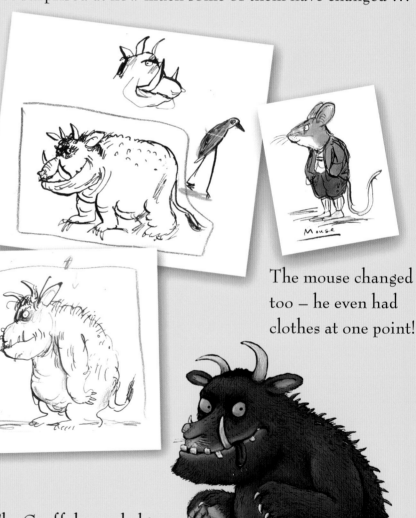

The mouse changed too — he even had clothes at one point!

The Gruffalo needed to be scary, but not too scary. My editor thought that some of my early drawings were too frightening, so I changed him a bit. But he's still a monster!

The Gruffalo's Child

Do all gruffalos have poisonous warts? I had to decide when Julia wrote *The Gruffalo's Child*. I decided that gruffalos get warts when they are older, so the Gruffalo's Child doesn't have one but she does already have small horns. She has yellow eyes, pink prickles and no knobbly knees. She looks different from her dad – and different in the finished book from when I first drew her, too.

The Witch

The witch in *Room on the Broom* does have a wart on the end of her nose but hers is not poisonous. And she didn't have it on my first sketches. She had different clothes too – her hat wasn't so tall and she wore a jacket not a cape.

At one point I drew her using her broom to sweep, which she doesn't do in the final book.

Why don't you have a go at drawing your very own Gruffalo, witch or Gruffalo's Child? Will they look just like mine, or will they be a little different too?

It's a Squash and a Squeeze!

Wise old man, won't you help me, please?
My house is a squash and a squeeze.

In the book *A Squash and a Squeeze* a little old lady brings four animals inside her house, then takes them all out again. Her house seems much bigger once they've gone! Make these fun farm animals out of card and tell the story yourself.

You will need:

- thin white card or stiff paper
- safety scissors
- glue
- coloured pens/pencils/paints
- tracing paper
- a shoe box
- a grown-up helper

1. Trace the shapes of the hen, the goat, the pig and the cow from pages 48, 49 and 50 onto the tracing paper. The goat has two main parts: one for the head, and one for the body.

2. Glue the tracing paper onto the white card or paper.

3. When the glue is dry, carefully cut out the animal shapes.

46

4. Using coloured pens, pencils or paints, colour in the animals on the white card side, looking at the pictures as a guide. Draw on the animals' eyes and noses with a black pen. Glue the goat's head onto the body.

5. Fold the shapes in half (along the central dotted line) so that each animal can stand up. The tracing paper should be on the inside. It helps to score a line first on the tracing paper side of the shape, using a ruler and the pointed end of your scissors. Ask a grown-up to do this for you.

6. Cut out each animal's ears, tails and horns and glue them on.

7. Take the shoe box and remove the lid. This will be your house. Draw and colour a door. Then ask a grown-up to cut down one side of the door and across the bottom so that it can open. Use pens to add a window to the house.

8. Finally, take your animals and tell the story of *A Squash and a Squeeze* by placing the hen, the goat, the pig and the cow inside the house – and then taking them out!

You could pretend to be the old lady!

47

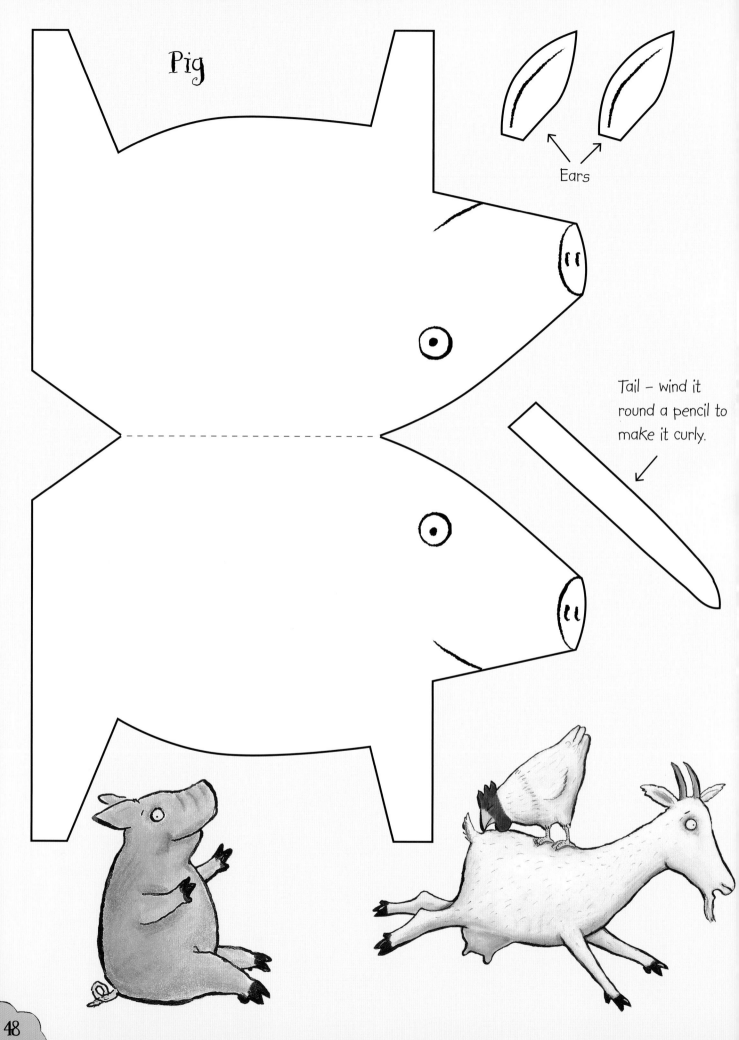

Pig

Ears

Tail – wind it
round a pencil to
make it curly.

48

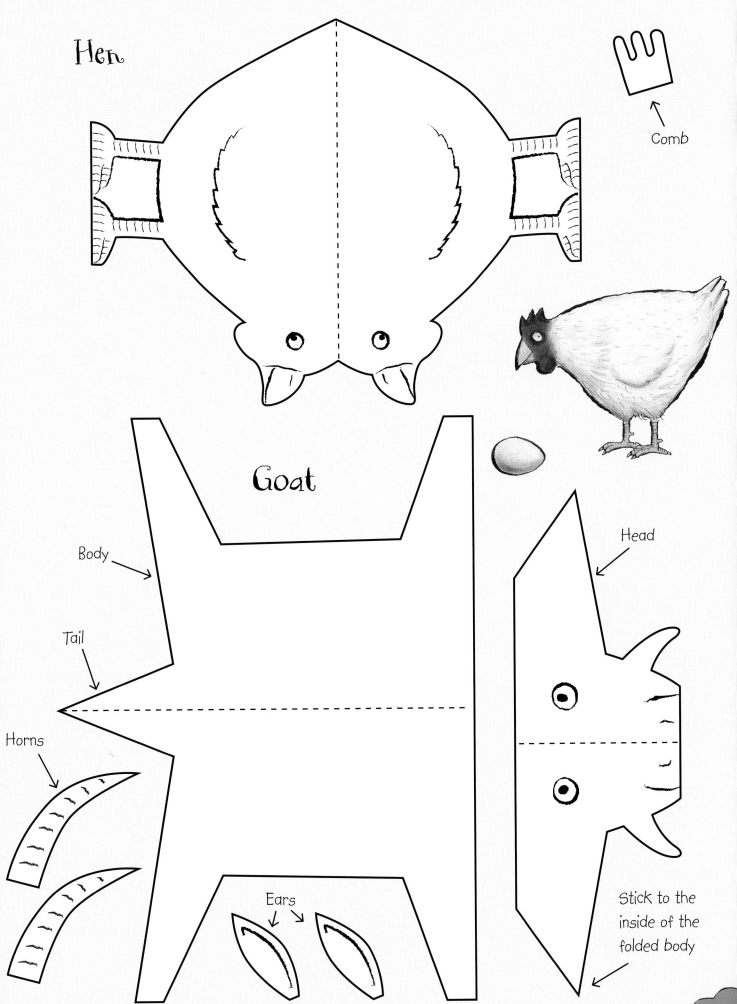

Hen

Comb

Goat

Body

Head

Tail

Horns

Ears

Stick to the inside of the folded body

49

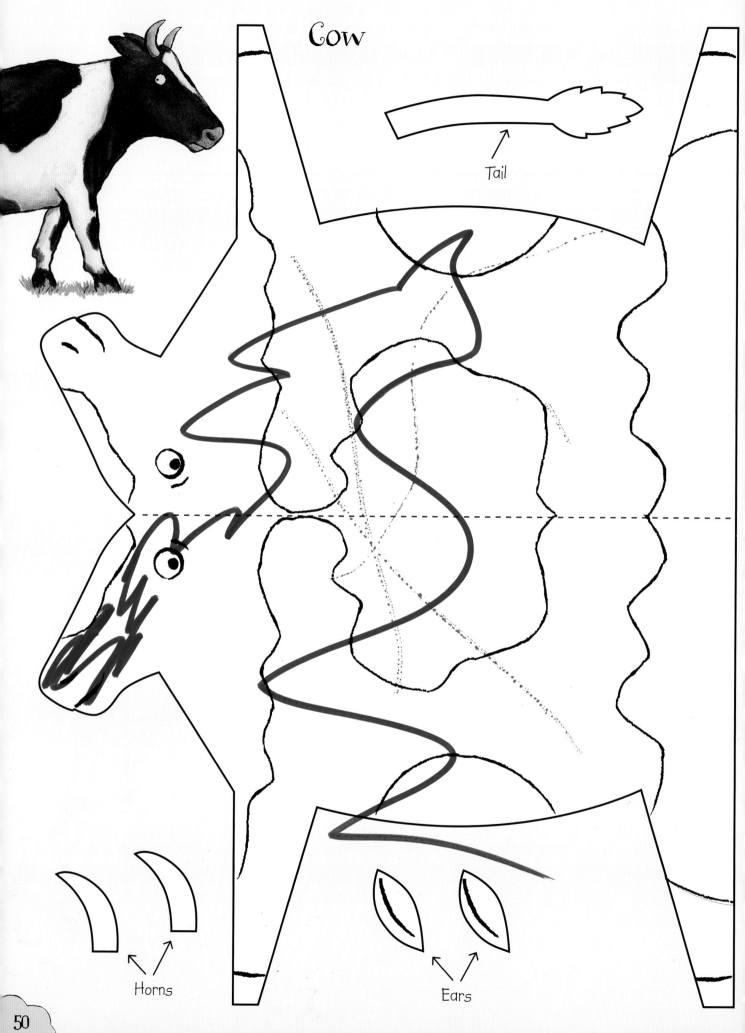

Cow

Tail

Horns

Ears

Animal Sounds

Can you draw lines to match the hen, the goat, the pig and the cow to the sounds they make?

What other animal sounds can you make?

The little old lady has a hen, a goat, a pig and a cow. These animals can often be found on a farm.

Hens

On a farm, hens usually live together in a hen house. You'll know where the hen house is because you'll hear lots of loud clucking! Hens lay eggs, which the farmer collects. Hens usually lay about 250 eggs in one year, but some can lay more than 300! Most hens can fly a little bit but only for a short distance.

Goats

Goats are very curious creatures. They like to explore and they will try to eat almost anything. Goats are very good at balancing and they can also jump quite high. Some goats can even climb trees! Most goats have two small horns and a beard. Like cows, they make milk that we can drink.

Pigs

Pigs have curly tails and wide, flat noses called snouts. Pigs have an amazing sense of smell and love to snuffle around with their snouts. They make noises which sound like grunts and oinks. You'll often see pigs rolling around in mud. The mud cools them down and protects their skin from the sun.

Cows

Moo! Can you hear the herd of cows in the field? Cows can spend up to eight hours a day chewing on grass. A female cow produces milk, which humans use to make yogurt, cheese, butter and lots of other tasty foods. A male cow is called a bull and a young cow is called a calf.

Can you think of any other animals that live on a farm?

Describe George

Do you know the story of *The Smartest Giant in Town*?
George the giant gets some lovely new clothes, but on the way
home he gives them away to some animals that need his help.

Can you circle the words that describe George?

nice

helpful

kind

angry

tall

small

rude

friendly

Answers on page 61

The Smartest Giant in Town

George deserves a treat for being so kind.
Can you design a fantastic new outfit for him?

You look great, George!

George's Animal Friends

George helped lots of different animals. Can you fill in the missing letters and then draw lines to match the animals to their names?

e_g

gira__e

f_sh

mou_e

_oat

Answers on page 61.

Odd One Out

George is looking for a smart new shirt. One of these shirts is different from the others. Can you find it?

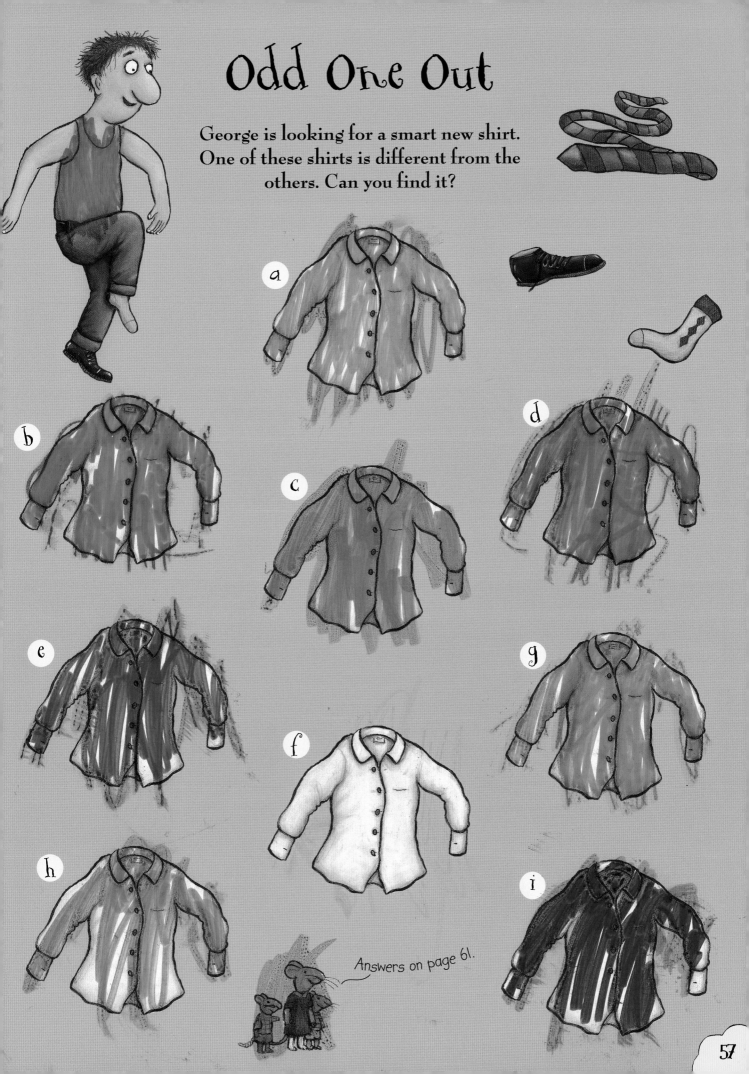

a

b

c

d

e

f

g

h

i

Answers on page 61.

Creature Challenge

How much can you remember about all the
different creatures that are in this book?
Try this fun quiz to find out.

1 Which of these animals *doesn't*
live in the deep dark wood?

   a. Owl ☐

   b. Fox ☐

   c. Crocodile ☐

2 Which is the biggest animal in
the world?

   a. Blue whale ☐

   b. Elephant ☐

   c. Giraffe ☐

3 How many tentacles does
an octopus have?

   a. 6 ☐

   b. 8 ☐

   c. 10 ☐

4 How do bats like to sleep?

   a. Upside down ☐

   b. In a bed ☐

   c. In a nest ☐

5 Can you name an animal that …

☐ … is furry?

☐ … has feathers?

☐ … has scaly skin?

When you think of an animal, tick the box and give yourself 1 point.

6 A butterfly is an insect. How many legs does it have?

   a. 8 ☐

   b. 4 ☐

   c. 6 ☐

7 Can you name three creatures that live in the sea?

When you think of an animal, tick the box and give yourself 1 point.

☐ ☐ ☐

8 Which of these animals lays eggs?

a. Cow ☐

b. Hen ☐

c. Pig ☐

9 What sort of noise does a frog make?

a. It hoots ☐

b. It croaks ☐

c. It squeaks ☐

10 What colour are the Gruffalo's prickles?

a. Blue ☐

b. Green ☐

c. Purple ☐

Now count the number of points you have got.

0-4
Have another go
Good try! You can't remember everything about the creatures in this book but that doesn't matter. Why not try the quiz again?

5-9
Pat on the back
Well done! You know a lot about the amazing world of animals. And there's so much more to find out!

10-14
You're a star
Wow! You know so much about all the incredible creatures in the world. What a clever creature you are!

Answers on page 61.

Answers

Page 6: Story Match
1:a, 2: f, 3: e, 4: h, 5: b, 6: d, 7: g, 8: c.

Page 10: Count and Colour
5 claws, 2 eyes, 4 legs, 3 teeth.

Page 21: Let's Go On a Broom Ride

START

FINISH

Page 24: Match the Sea Creatures
1: Seagull, 2: Crabs, 3: Fish, 4: Octopus, 5: Dolphins, 6: Seals, 7: Lobster, 8: Starfish, 9: Penguins, 10: Turtle.

Page 34: Rainforest Crossword

```
              ¹F
   ²S P I D E R
   N          O
 ³B A T        G
   K
⁴E L E ⁵P H A N T
       A
⁶B U T T E R F L Y
       R
       R
       O
     ⁷A N T
```

Page 35: Colourful Creatures
The matching butterfly: 2, matching bug: 4, matching caterpillar: 5, matching frog: 3.

Pages 40/41: Charlie Cook Returns his Books
The crocodile has six teeth.
The three bears are looking for Goldilocks.
Charlie is returning four books to the library.

Pages 42/43: Spot the Difference

Page 54: Describe George
The words that describe him are: tall, kind, friendly, helpful, nice.

Page 56: George's Animal Friends
Goat, mouse, fox, dog, giraffe.

Page 57: Odd One Out
Shirt i has only four buttons.

Page 58/59/60: Creature Challenge
1: c, 2: a, 3: b, 4: a, 5: Score a point for each animal you can think of, up to 3 points, 6: c, 7: Score a point for each animal you can think of, up to 3 points, 8: b, 9: b, 10: c.